Juicing for Weight Loss

Unlock the Power of Juicing to Lose Massive Weight, Stimulate Healing, and Feel Amazing in Your Body

By Kira Novac (ISBN: 978-1-80095-020-7)

Copyright ©Kira Novac 2015

Table of contents

Introduction

Juicing is a great way to preserve the vitamins, nutrients, and enzymes that your body needs, which both fruits and vegetables naturally have. Why should you bother juicing when you could always cook these vegetables? Well, recent studies have shown that these essential enzymes and nutrients are often destroyed through cooking. If you eat the whole vegetable raw, on the other hand, your body's natural digestion might not be able to break them down in the most efficient way. Juicing solves all these problems by helping you squeeze the most out of the produce you buy!

To top everything off, juicing is just plain fun! It's a great way to trick your kids (and yourself) into eating things they wouldn't normally eat. Unfortunately, most people also think it tastes incredibly bad. So how should you trick yourself into eating it? Why not try juicing the vegetables with some delicious and tasty fruits?

Juicing is now a popular method of staying healthy and (if desired) losing weight because of several reasons. One, juicing makes it easy for people to consume vegetables, especially if they don't love the taste of these foods. Juicing changes the texture of the vegetables, which is what often turns people off to them. It also can mask the tastes you don't like using fruit and other sweeter tasting juice.

Two, juicing is a lot easier and healthier than when you cook vegetables because it only takes minutes to make a nutrient-packed meal or snack. In fact, the juicing process is easy. You only need a food processor or juicer, place all the vegetables in, and squeeze their juices out. Compared to cooking the veggies, juicing fruits and vegetables is more nutrient-packed because you are really extracting all the essential nutrients from these food items and taking away the rough fibrous material, meaning that your body has a much easier path to do the digestive process. This is why many people get hooked on juicing- it's nutrient packed and will give you long-lasting energy. It's much more sustainable than coffee or other caffeinated drinks that can only give you a short boost of energy terminated by a subsequent energy crash and very often sugar cravings.

And finally, juicing is extremely helpful in weight loss, which is probably one of the major concerns and goals of most people today. Why? Again, think of all the nutrition, antioxidants and alkalizing properties that feeding your body with natural juices brings! Remember that if your main goal is weight loss, you need to focus on juicing vegetables, lots of leafy greens as well as fruit that is low in sugar (for example lemons, limes, grapefruits, pomegranates). You can add some other fruit to taste, however juicing fruit high in sugar is not always good for you. It's better to have this fruit as a whole or use it in a smoothie to drink it with its natural fiber.

There is a lot of hype going on. Marketers try to sell you some magical green smoothie cleanses as well as juicing recipes, but in this day and age it's hard to find a reliable source of information. This is a big concern of mine, and a reason why I wrote this book.

Here's a really simple rule that will dramatically help you in your weight loss and health goals through juicing:

- Focus on juicing vegetables as much as possible
- Choose fruits naturally low in sugar
- Add spices and herbs to your juices (for example ginger, mint, and basil)
- Add good oils to your juices (yes, don't fear good fats), coconut oil, cold-pressed virgin olive oil and avocado oil are great choices

Why juicing fruit high in sugar is bad for you?

Research has shown that fructose without fiber (fruit juices, as juicing deprives fruit of its natural fiber) causes absolute havoc in the body (inflammation, acidity, insulin resistance). It doesn't matter if it was a homemade juice. Sugar is sugar.

Fruit high in sugar can be added to your juices in small amounts only, to help you get used to juicing and improve the taste of your experiments. As you juice more and more, your taste buds will change. For example, I can juice some red bell peppers, ginger, zucchini, lettuce and a carrot and I am in heaven. I find this mix really sweet actually! So avoid recipes that tell you to juice sugary fruits like kiwis or pineapples in huge amounts.

Imagine what happens when you juice fruits rich in sugar... When you remove the fiber, the liquid juice is absorbed into your blood stream much quicker than it does with fiber. This is why, if you are juicing fruits, it will lead to unstable blood sugar levels and a drop in blood sugar. This, in turn, will lead to low energy levels and even sugar cravings.

Exception: You can have an occasional orange juice or something similar, but make sure you dilute it in some water.

Pure orange juice is not that good for you, especially if you want to lose weight.

Benefits of Juicing

-Fruits and vegetables are the foundations of good health, and juicing allows even the most committed carnivore the opportunity to get the daily recommended amount of fruits and vegetables. If you decide to start juicing only once a day, you can still expect to reap many benefits. So remember this rule - one juice a day will keep the doctor away!

-The entire point of juicing is to give your digestive tract and associated organs involved in digestion, energy production, and waste control (colon, kidneys, liver, bladder, intestines) a break. This leads to a healthier digestive system.

-Juicing removes the fiber from your fruits and vegetables, which allows instant absorption of nutrients and a quick conversion to energy in the blood. Again, this is why I have previously stressed the importance of focusing on fruits that are low in sugar. With all the fiber taken away from your juice, you don't want to feed your body with sugar (sugar is sugar, even though natural, even though it's fructose - it's still sugar, this is why juicing fruits high in sugar is fatal not only for health but also for weight loss).

Exception: you can add some fruit to taste. Let's say you want to juice some spinach. I don't know about you, but I am not naturally attracted to the taste of spinach. This is why I like to add an apple, some ginger and some mint leaves for better taste. It changes the game.

Common question- why bother to juice if you can just eat those fruits and vegetables in their raw form or make a smoothie?

Answer- yes, you could do that and yes, it would be healthy. The problem is - would you be able to eat 2 cups of spinach, 1 cup of kale, 3 grapefruits, 3 cucumbers, 2 apples and 2 tomatoes at a time? First of all, it could take you an eternity to drool through such a salad and secondly, your body would need some time to digest it (even though it's healthy and natural). However, if you juice the above mentioned ingredients, you give your body a really quick injection of nutrients. I call it shots of health.

Important - I am not saying that from now on, all you should do is juice and that juicing is the only path to wellness, health and optimal weight loss. Instead, you need to see juicing as a natural tool and a new, healthy habit that you need to develop for your own good. You can still have smoothies (that is blended fruits or vegetables with all their fiber in), and you can still have salads and raw veggies. We want balance.

This is not a book on juice cleanse. All kinds of cleanses, especially if you have certain health condition you want to address, should be conducted under your doctor's supervision. It's not that you get a recipe book and get some information online or hire an online health coach and do everything by yourself. Well, you could do that, if your goal is to simply live a healthier life and learn new recipes and habits, then a good health coach can help you. But if you have been dealing with any kind of a health problem, you need to work with your doctor as well. You can also seek advice from a naturopathy doctor.

Now, let's carry on with the benefits of juicing. I am sure they will boost your motivation so that you never part with your juicer.

-The energy spent on digestion and converting food to blood sugar (about 30 percent blood sugar in the body) can be diverted to other activities. This means you will have more energy and stamina on the days you have fresh juice. You can take this new energy to the gym, do things you are passionate about, or spend more time with your family.

-The quick absorption of nutrients means they are delivered more quickly to cells, facilitating any repair and healing. Easily accessible antioxidants from many different fruits and vegetables can quickly reduce the damage caused by free radicals in the blood, as well as reduce the risk of cancer, heart disease, diabetes, asthma, and autoimmune diseases.

-Regular juicing with a range of vibrant, colorful produce, which contain many nutrients as well as antioxidants, can reduce the risk of age-related diseases, such as macular degeneration, cataracts, and arthritis.

Also, it is important to know and understand how juicing can actually benefit or contribute to weight loss.

How Juicing Can Help You Lose Weight

Through Concentrated Nutrients.

The reason why weight loss can be difficult to achieve sometimes is because the body does not get the right amount of nutrients that can help it lose weight. Many people go on fad diets and instead of feeding their body with quality nutrients, get paranoid about food and try to starve themselves and reduce calories (it's not about eating less, it's about eating right).

However, when you juice fruits low in sugar and vegetables, especially green vegetables, you get all the necessary nutrients that can help lose weight in a more concentrated form, because the juice is from the whole fruit or vegetable and there are no added ingredients. Therefore, because the body gets these concentrated nutrients, losing weight is more effective. You have more energy and less sugar and crappy food cravings. In addition, you are in a better mood. Nice combination, right? You see, the reason why we crave unhealthy foods is that our body lacks nutrients in the first place. It's sending some really annoying signals, "Feed me more; I am still hungry." Unfortunately, most people feed their bodies with empty calories and processed foods that only add to the vicious cycle. So, again, give your body some intelligent nutrition. You deserve it. It's not that from now on, you

9

will have to survive entirely on juices. No. Just try to add 1-2 cups a day and slowly but steadily work your way to a healthy lifestyle. Baby steps.

Through Strong Detoxifying Properties

When you juice fruits and vegetables, the detoxifying properties are very strong and this can help the body excrete away toxins that may only hamper weight loss.

Through Fat-Burning Properties

Just like the detoxifying properties, some fruits (especially grapefruits, limes, lemons, tomatoes and pomegranate) and vegetables (especially green veggies and leafy greens) have fat burning abilities and since you get these nutrients in a more concentrated form, you also get more of these fat burning properties making it easy for you to burn fats and lose weight.

Through Appetite-Suppressant Properties.

The reason why most people find it hard to lose weight sometimes is the fact that they have large appetites that they fail to control. Some fruits and vegetables are very good appetite suppressants, especially when you drink these juiced foods before a meal. This way, your anxious appetite is suppressed and instead of eating too much of what's not good for you, you focus on healthy food in amounts you actually need to support all bodily functions which can help you lose weight.

Through Easy Digestion

Another reason why losing weight can be difficult at times is because eating solid foods can be very difficult to digest, especially if you have very low metabolism. Therefore, instead of burning fats easily your body ends up storing them. But if you do juicing, you'll naturally consume a lighter meal or snack than solid foods since this is liquid form already. Because they are in liquid form already, they make it easier for the body to digest them and distribute all the necessary health and weight loss nutrients.

Through Properties that Save Sugar

Some fruits and vegetables have natural sweeteners in them so that when you juice them, they will taste good already even without adding sugar to your juice. Since you are no longer adding sugar to your juice, you are helping your body lose weight effectively as you are not adding burden to it through the consumption of sugar. You already know that sugar is one of the reasons why it is sometimes difficult to lose weight as sugar is known to make you fat. When juicing, you get just enough sugar to tickle your taste buds but not enough to hamper weight loss. I especially recommend juicing red bell peppers or adding some carrots. It usually does the trick for me when adding sweetness.

Through Ease in Consumption

Another reason why it is difficult to lose weight is because people tend to get discouraged with the many weight loss regimens out there, especially if they find these programs and diet plans hard to follow. For instance, there are diet plans and programs forcing people to consume fruits and vegetables even if they cannot tolerate their tastes. That's not the way it should be and if you only rely on your willpower, it can be a really tough journey. As mentioned, when you juice fruits and vegetables, it is easier to consume them since it only takes one gulp and no need to chew them. Easy peasy lemon squeezy!

With the combination of fruits, vegetables are made even tastier. So, even if losing weight through juicing may require fruits and vegetables, you are still going to succeed in losing weight since you will be more willing to consume the juiced form.

Through Natural and Safe Weight Loss Effects

Many people get discouraged in losing weight and even fail to lose weight because instead of helping them lose weight, some of their prescribed supplements only resulted in side effects as they are not purely natural. However, through juicing, you can successfully lose weight since you are consuming fruits and veggies naturally and there are no side effects that could hamper your quest to weight loss. You will also be more encouraged to truly lose weight considering the safety of this method.

By drinking just a cup and a half of juice each day, you'll be more than compensated for the recommended daily vegetable allowance. Get healthy TODAY!

Free Complimentary Recipe eBook

Thank you so much for taking an interest in my work!

As a thank you, I would love to offer you a free complimentary recipe eBook to help you achieve vibrant health. It will teach you how to prepare amazingly tasty and healthy gluten-free treats so that you never feel deprived or bored again!

As a special bonus, you will be able to receive all my future books (kindle format) for free or only $0.99.

Download your free recipe eBook here:

http://bit.ly/gluten-free-desserts-book

Juice Recipes

Rich and Creamy Breakfast Juice
Serves: 2

If you want to be sure your body gets all the essential fats it needs, this juice is a great choice. It combines the health-giving properties of apples and carrots with the rich natural flavor of coconut, alkaline benefits of spinach, and the brightness of ginger. You can substitute commercial canned coconut milk if fresh coconut isn't available, but make sure you choose a brand with no added water, gums or preservatives.

Ingredients:

- Meat from ½ large coconut or 1 small coconut
- 2 medium carrots
- 1/2 green apple
- ½ cup spinach
- ½ inch fresh ginger

Procedure:

1. Grate the coconut using a hand grater or food processor. Add the grated coconut to a blender or juicer, along with about 1/3 cup water.

2. Process until the mixture becomes very thick and the coconut is in many tiny pieces. Place the coconut and water mixture into your juicer using the fine screen. Run it through the juicer, allowing the screen to extract the coconut meat. You may need to remove the end piece to allow the coconut to pass through freely. Reserve the coconut meat for later use.

3. Remove the seeds from the apple and add it to the juicer or a blender along with the spinach, carrots and ginger.

4. Process until an opaque orange liquid is produced.

5. Pour in 1/3 cup of fresh coconut milk, mixing thoroughly. Garnish with slivers of fresh ginger. For a thicker product, refrigerate the liquid first.

Shooting Star
Serves: 2

Just perfect for mornings!

Ingredients:

- ¼ inch ginger root
- ½ lemon, peeled
- 2 grapefruits, peeled
- 5 carrots, sliced
- ½ cup lettuce

Procedure:

1. Press the ingredients through a juicer.
2. Stir to combine.
3. Serve with ice, if preferred.

Grapefruit Zinger
Serves: 2

Feeling energized!

Ingredients:

- ½ cup sparkling water
- 2 grapefruits, peeled
- ½ inch ginger
- ½ pear, sliced
- ½ cup blueberries

Procedure:

1. Press the ingredients through a blender.
2. Stir to combine.
3. Serve with ice, if preferred.

Orange Carrot Juice
Serves: 2

Take a sip of vitamins A and C! Great for the skin and you're your eyes!

Ingredients:

- 1 orange, peeled
- 8 carrots, sliced
- 1 cup kale
- 1 beet

Procedure:

1. Press the ingredients through a juicer.
2. Stir to combine.
3. Serve with ice, if preferred.

Berry Powerful Juice
Serves: 2

Grapes and berries make a flavorful juice that supplies plenty of antioxidant compounds, but they can't provide all the nutrition your body needs. Besides, grapes are rich in sugar and should only be used as an addition to your juice to make it taste better. That's why combining them with fresh dark leafy greens such as kale or spinach is such a smart idea especially if you are new to juicing greens. These vegetables give you more energy and help you avoid running out of power midway through the day. They also combine well with the fruit, avoiding the bitter taste that sometimes comes with leafy greens alone.

Ingredients:

- 2 cups blueberries or raspberries
- ½ cup red or Concord grapes
- 1 cup fresh kale
- 1 cup fresh spinach

Procedure:

1. Wash the fruit thoroughly. Remove the grapes from their stems and discard the stems.
2. Remove any wilted or yellow leaves from the kale and spinach. Process all the fruit and vegetables in a juicer or powerful blender, adding water if necessary.
3. Chill and drink along with a light snack. Add 2 tablespoons of your favorite vegan protein powder for a meal replacement drink.

Beet Beauty
Serves: 2

Real beauty comes from inside. To your health, it will take care of the rest!

Ingredients:

- 1-inch ginger root
- 1 apple, cored, and sliced
- 2 carrots, sliced
- 2 beets with greens

Procedure:

1. Press the ingredients through a juicer.
2. Stir to combine.
3. Serve with ice, if preferred.

Grapefruit and Green Grape Juice
Serves: 2-4

Healthy and packed with flavor!

Ingredients:

- 1 wedge lemon, peeled
- 1 cup green grapes, seedless
- 3 grapefruits, cored, and sliced
- Half cup coconut water

Procedure:

1. Press the ingredients through a juicer.
2. Add some coconut water. Stir to combine.
3. Serve with ice, if preferred.

Nutritious Peach Juice
Serves: 2

Fresh summer peaches are a sweet, sticky favorite for many people, but they get even better on a foundation of powerful, nutritious green vegetables. This flavorful juice includes strong-tasting fruits that effectively cover the taste of nutrition-packed greens like broccoli and spinach. While the color of this juice recipe might be a little surprising, the flavor and nutrient profile simply can't be beat. Try it on its own, or as a quick vitamin shot along with an ordinary meal. Using only the broccoli stalks allows you to reserve the more-tender florets for use in salads or other healthy recipes.

Ingredients:

- 1 ripe peach
- 1 apple
- 1 grapefruit
- 2 broccoli stalks
- 1 cup spinach leaves

Procedure:

1. Wash all fruits and vegetables thoroughly. Remove the tough ends of the broccoli, the pits from the peaches, and the seeds from the apples.
2. Place all ingredients in a juicer and process until smooth. The result may be slightly brownish in color, but the flavor will be nice. Enjoy!

Red Racer
Serves: 2

Pacify your sweet tooth in a sugar-free way!

Ingredients:

- 1 cup pomegranates
- 2 red bell peppers
- 2 lemons, peeled

Procedure:

1. Press the ingredients through an electric juicer.
2. Stir to combine.
3. Serve with ice, if preferred.

Ginger Pear Juice
Serves: 2

Simple, anti-inflammatory mix that everyone will love!

Ingredients:

- 1 medium pear
- 1 stalk celery
- 1 tablespoon fresh ginger
- ½ cup romaine lettuce

Procedure:

1. Wash all ingredients and remove the stem and seeds from the pear.
2. Combine the fruit, lettuce, and ginger in a blender or juicer, processing until smooth. For a creamier texture, add a few ice cubes.

Green Carrot
Serves: 2

Easy way to sneak in some greens into your diet!

Ingredients:

- 1 cup spinach
- ½ apple, cored, and sliced
- ½ cucumber with skin
- 2 ribs celery with leaves
- 2 carrots, sliced

Procedure:

1. Press the ingredients through a juicer.
2. Stir to combine.
3. Serve with ice, if preferred.
4. Great for the blood!

Cucumber and Apple Zinger
Serves: 2

Quick and easy tonic! Cucumbers are excellent for hydration!

Ingredients:

- 1-inch ginger root
- 4 organic cucumbers with skin
- 1 apple, cored, and sliced

Procedure:

1. Press the ingredients through a juicer.
2. Stir to combine.
3. Serve with ice, if preferred.

Hearty Sweet Potato
Serves: 2-3

Sweet potatoes may seem like an unlikely choice for juice, but they provide plenty of vitamin A and folate.

Ingredients:

- 2 sweet tangerines
- 2 sweet golden apples, such as Golden Delicious
- 3 large carrots
- 1 cup spinach
- 1 medium raw sweet potato
- 1 medium red bell pepper

Procedure:

1. Peel the tangerines and remove any seeds. Wash all the other ingredients thoroughly. Cut off the stem ends of the carrots and pepper, removing the seeds and ribs from the pepper.

2. Remove the stem and seeds from the apples and peel the sweet potato, cutting it into large cubes.

3. Process all of the ingredients in a juicer.

4. Enjoy!

Green Energizer Bunny
Serve: 2-3

Powerful, alkaline, and anti-inflammatory.

Ingredients:

- 1-inch ginger root
- ½ cup spinach
- ½ cup kale
- ¼ head romaine lettuce
- ¼ bunch celery
- ¼ fennel bulb
- ½ lemon, peeled
- ½ cucumber with skin
- 2 apples, cored, and sliced

Procedure:

1. Press the ingredients through a juicer.
2. Stir to combine.
3. Serve with ice, if preferred.

Refreshing Red Bell Pepper Carrot Juice
Serves: 2

Bell peppers are rich in vitamin C, which play a significant role in eye and gum health. They also contain vitamin A, which is instrumental for healthy skin.

Ingredients:

- 4 medium carrots
- 1 medium green apple
- A few kale leaves
- A few cabbage leaves
- 2 large red bell peppers

Procedure:

1. Peel, cut, deseed, and/or chop the ingredients as needed.
2. Feed the ingredients one at a time, in the order listed, through the juicer.
3. Stir the juice and pour into glasses to serve.

Keeps you going and going and going!

Hangover Juice
Serves: 2-3

Rough night? Try this recipe!

Ingredients:

- 1 cup broccoli, shredded into florets
- 1 cup cauliflower, shredded into florets
- 2 cucumbers (no need to peel if organic)
- 1 apple, cored, and sliced

Procedure:

1. Press the ingredients through a juicer.
2. Stir to combine.
3. Serve with ice, if preferred.

Tomato Gazpacho Juice
Serves: 2-4

Though gazpacho is traditionally served as a cold soup, in this recipe it transforms into a tasty beverage. Tomatoes contain over nine thousand different phytonutrients, including vitamin C, copper, iron, potassium, and magnesium. They are also a good source of lycopene, which may help prevent cancer and improve mental health.

Ingredients:

- 6 plum tomatoes
- 2 large stalks celery
- 1 seedless cucumber
- 1 medium carrot
- 1 small red bell pepper
- ½ bunch parsley leaves
- 1 lime
- 1 green onion

Procedure:

1. Peel, cut, deseed, and/or chop the ingredients as needed.
2. Place a container under the juicer's spout.
3. Feed the ingredients one at a time, in the order listed through the juicer.
4. Stir the juice and pour into glasses to serve.

Festive Fruit and Vegetable Juice
Serves: 2

This juice includes all kinds of nutritious and colorful fruits and vegetables in a delicious mixture. It'll help you increase your intake of all those important dietary elements without any trouble. If you choose to use the beet greens, choose younger specimens with a milder flavor.

Ingredients:

- 3 medium carrots
- 2 ripe yellow pears
- 2 sweet red apples
- 1 medium beet, with or without greens
- 1 ripe red tomato
- 2 leaves arugula
- ½ small head cauliflower
- ½ small head broccoli

Procedure:

1. Wash all the ingredients thoroughly. Trim off the stem and root ends of the beet and carrots. Remove all the seeds from the apples and pears. Peel the pineapple and remove the core.

2. Juice all ingredients, adding the broccoli, cauliflower, arugula and beet greens along with wetter ingredients such as apples and carrots. Thin with water as desired and drink at room temperature.

Heartburn Helper
Serves: 2

Easy, simple and effective. What more can you want?

Ingredients:

- 4 carrots, sliced
- 1 cup spinach
- ½ inch ginger

Procedure:

1. Press the ingredients through an electric juicer.
2. Stir to combine.
3. Serve with ice, if preferred.

Alkaline juicing helps with heartburn and leafy greens mixed with ginger offers the best of Alkalinity!

Good Morning Juice
Serves: 2

Start the day the right way!

Ingredients:

- 1 inch ginger root
- ¼ cup mint leaves
- 1 cucumber with skin
- 3 carrots, sliced
- Sea salt to taste

Procedure:

1. Press the produce through a juicer.
2. Season with salt to taste.
3. Stir to combine.
4. Serve with ice, if preferred.

Super Tomato Juice
Serves: 2

This juice is a great choice if you feel like snacking. You can also serve it as a side dish.

Ingredients:

- ½ cucumber, peeled
- 1 red pepper, seeded, and sliced
- 3 carrots, sliced
- 3 tomatoes, sliced
- ¼ teaspoon salt
- Hot sauce to taste

Procedure:

1. Press the produce through a juicer.
2. Season with sea salt.
3. Add hot sauce to taste.
4. Stir to combine.

Parsley Power Gulp
Serves: 2

Often used as a garnish rather than an essential ingredient in recipes, parsley actually has a number of significant health benefits. It's an excellent source of folate, which helps to prevent certain cancers, and it has diuretic properties to flush excess water from the body. Parsley is also one of the best natural sources for vitamin C.

Ingredients:

- 1 bunch parsley leaves
- 4 medium carrots
- 2 large stalks celery
- 1 small apple

Procedure:

1. Peel, cut, deseed, and/or chop the ingredients as needed.
2. Feed the ingredients one at a time, in the order listed through the juicer.

3. Stir the juice and pour into glasses to serve.

Spicy Apple Lemonade
Serves: 2

This flavorful fruit juice includes a sweet yellow pepper to boost its nutritional value. You'll enjoy the cleansing effects of this beverage, as well as its mild, pleasant flavor. To increase tartness, simply add another lemon to the mix.

Ingredients:

- 2 large sweet apples, such as Fuji
- 1 lemon
- 1 cup lettuce
- 1 sweet yellow bell pepper
- 1 tablespoon ginger

Procedure:

1. Peel the lemon and remove any seeds. Wash the pepper, lettuce, and apples thoroughly to get rid of dirt and chemical residues.

2. Seed all the apples and remove the seeds, stem and interior ribs from the pepper.

3. Add all ingredients to a powerful juicer with a large screen and process until smooth. Drink chilled.

Sunshine
Serves: 2

Helps protect your skin from the sun!

Ingredients:

- ½ cup parsley sprigs
- 1 sweet potato, chopped
- 3 carrots, chopped
- Salt and black pepper to taste

Procedure:

1. Press the produce through a juicer.
2. Season with salt and black pepper to taste.
3. Stir to combine.
4. Serve with ice, if preferred.

Red Summer Cooler
Serves: 4

This interesting juice recipe combines the classic pairing of tomatoes and basil with sweet red strawberries. The best berries are organic, local, and in season, but if these aren't available you can choose fragrant berries and wash them well. Garnish the finished juice with mint for greater complexity and even more great phytonutrients.

Ingredients:

- 1 pound ripe red tomatoes
- 1 cup whole strawberries
- ¼ cup leaves of sweet basil

Procedure:

1. Hull the strawberries and tomatoes, discarding the leaves. If necessary, cut the tomatoes into pieces your juicer is able to handle.

2. Process the fruit and basil leaves together to produce a strikingly red, flavorful beverage. Serve over ice. Kids love it!

Power Gulp
Serves: 2

Great for detox and proper hydration-and *before/after Workouts!*

Ingredients:

- ½ cup clean, filtered water
- 1 cup green grapes, seedless
- 1 cup kale, sliced
- 1 apple, cored, and diced
- 1 cucumber, peeled, and sliced
- Optional: a few drops of liquid chlorophyll
- Optional: hemp powder protein

Procedure:

1. Using a blender, process all the ingredients until smooth.
2. Push the juice through a strainer.
3. Stir to combine.
4. Serve with ice, and garnish with cucumber slices.

5. If you want, add some liquid chlorophyll and hemp protein powder.

Total Health Booster
Serves: 2

Drink up, and shape up!

Ingredients:

- ½ cup cherries, fresh, and pitted
- 1 cup spinach
- 1 cup lettuce
- 1 apple

Procedure:

1. Using a blender, process all the ingredients until smooth.
2. Push the juice through a strainer.
3. Stir to combine.
4. Serve with ice, and garnish with additional cherries.

Vegetable Citrus Medley
Serves: 2

This drink is rich in a variety of vitamins, minerals and phytonutrients. While it uses vegetables more usually associated with soups and stews, that shouldn't put you off. The result is a complex beverage with an unusual color and plenty of health-promoting properties.

Ingredients:

- 2 large grapefruits
- 1 medium carrot
- 1 small lemon
- 1 stalk celery
- ½ cup raw red beets
- ½ cup spinach leaves

Procedure:

1. Peel the citrus fruits and remove any seeds. Wash the greens and other vegetables thoroughly.

2. Process the lemon and grapefruits first, followed by the leafy greens. Use the celery and carrots to push any leftover material through your juicer.

3. Serve over ice with ginger if desired.

Antioxidant Supreme
Serves: 2

Detox fast with this anti-inflammatory smoothie! Yes, I know, it's a book on juicing but since I actually created this recipe this morning, previous to writing this chapter, I just had to share it with you! It's great for breakfast!

Ingredients:

- ¼ cup coconut water
- 1 cup blueberries, fresh
- 1 cup spinach
- 2 teaspoons spirulina or barley grass green powder
- ½ cup coconut milk
- 1 teaspoon grated ginger

Procedure:

1. Using a blender, process all the ingredients until smooth.
2. Stir to combine.
3. Serve with ice, and garnish with mango slices.

Red Cabbage Carrot Juice
Serves: 2

Cabbage is one of very few vegetables that contain vitamin E. It's also a good source of sulfur, which helps to purify the blood and detoxify the liver.

Ingredients:

- 2 cups large Swiss chard leaves
- 4 large carrots
- 1 medium apple
- ¼ small head red cabbage
- tablespoons freshly squeezed lemon juice

Procedure:

1. Peel, cut, deseed, and/or chop the ingredients as needed.
2. Place a container under the juicer's spout.
3. Feed the Swiss chard, carrots, apple, and cabbage through the juicer.

4. Stir the lemon juice into the juice and pour into glasses to serve. Enjoy!

Energy Upper
Serves: 2

Simple yet effective!

Ingredients:

- 1/2 cup water to dilute the juice
- 1/2 cup peaches, fresh, and sliced
- 1 cup spinach
- Optional (but recommended for more energy): 2 teaspoons of spirulina

Procedure:

1. Place all the ingredients through a juicer.
2. Stir to combine and add some water and spirulina.
3. Stir again.
4. Serve with ice, if preferred.

Asian-Inspired Citrus Cabbage Blend
Serves: 2-4

Cabbage gets a bad reputation with many people due to its tendency to become sulfurous and bitter when overcooked. Fresh cabbage has a crisp texture and zesty flavor that makes it the star of some unusual salads as well as this delightful juice. The combination of tropical citrus, Asian pears and other Chinese ingredients will make this one of your favorite lunch or dinner-time juices.

Ingredients:

- 1 small bok choy head, napa or green cabbage
- 2 medium carrots
- 2 tart green apples
- 2 Persian limes
- 1 lemon
- 1 Asian pear
- 1 thumb-length of ginger

Procedure:

1. Peel the lemon and limes. Wash the cabbage, carrots, pear and apples thoroughly. Remove the seeds and stems from the apples and pear.

2. Cut off the stem end from the carrots and chop the cabbage into manageable chunks. Process all the ingredients in a juicer or blender, starting and finishing with an apple. Pour over ice and drink quickly.

Immune Booster
Serves: 2-4

Shields up!

Ingredients:

- 1 kiwi, peeled, and chopped
- 1 orange, peeled, and chopped
- 2 grapefruits, peeled, and chopped
- 2 lemons
- 1 cup coconut water to dilute the juice (better for weight loss)

Procedure:

1. Using a blender, process all the ingredients until smooth.
2. Push the juice through a strainer.
3. Add some coconut water and stir to combine.
4. Serve with ice, if preferred.

Hunger-Defeating Smoothie
Serves: 2

It's good to spice up your juicing routines with some hunger satisfying and energy providing smoothies. Why is a smoothie in a juicing book? Well, it's not possible to juice avocados and bananas, right? Yet this smoothie is packed with nutrition and will help you sneak in more greens into your diet. This recipe combines the best of juicing and smoothies and is much tastier for those who are just starting out and can't imagine drinking spinach smoothies with all the spinach fiber and taste in.

Ingredients:

- 2 cups spinach, juiced
- Half cup coconut water (great for weight loss)
- 1 lemon, juiced
- 1 banana
- 1 avocado
- 10 to 12 ice cubes
- 1 teaspoon ginger and cinnamon (anti-inflammatory properties)

Procedure:

1. First juice the lemon and spinach and set the juice aside.
2. Place avocado and banana in a blender adding spinach and lemon juice, ice cubes, and coconut water (can be also regular water and coconut milk).
3. Blend well. Stir and add ginger and cinnamon.

Workout Refueler
Serves: 2

Time to get buff!

Ingredients:

- ½ cup water or coconut water
- ¼ cup almonds, raw
- 1 apple, peeled, and diced
- 1 sweet potato, peeled, and chopped
- 2 oranges, peeled, and chopped

Procedure:

1. Using a blender, process all the ingredients until smooth.
2. Push the juice through a strainer.
3. Stir to combine.
4. Serve with ice, if preferred.

Mint Wake-Up Call
Serves: 2-3

While the name suggests a breakfast juice, you can enjoy this refreshing recipe at any time of the day. This juice combines morning staples like grapefruit and orange with hearty carrots and light-tasting celery. Topped off with the cool, bright taste of mint, this juice makes a great start to the day or an excellent choice to brighten up a slow evening. Use a large screen in your juicer to ensure you get plenty of fiber in your juice.

Ingredients:

- 2 juicing oranges (Valencia works well)
- 1 medium pink or white grapefruit
- 1 large carrot
- 1 stalk green celery
- ½ cup peppermint or spearmint leaves
- ½ cup water or coconut water to dilute the juice

Procedure:

1. Wash the celery and carrot, removing all grit. Remove the leaves from the mint stems to keep the color of the finished product consistent.

2. Peel the citrus. Combine all ingredients in the juicer, adding the mint before the carrot. Use the carrot to push the leafy material through the juicer.

3. Serve over ice and add some coconut water.

Spicy Orange Pineapple
Serves: 2

Your body will appreciate the vitamin C, pineapple enzymes and metabolism-boosting capsaicin. To produce a crisp smoothie, add a few ice cubes to the mixture in a blender.

Ingredients:

- 3 grapefruits
- 1/2 cup spinach
- 1 medium carrot
- A few pineapple slices
- 1 lime
- 2 small red peppers

Procedure:

1. Peel the citrus fruits and remove any seeds. Wash the carrot and remove any core or peel from the pineapple.
2. Combine all ingredients in a juicer. Dilute in some water or coconut water if desired.

Apple Squash Dessert Juice
Serves: 4

One of the biggest problems for many juice dieters is the difficulty of finding a satisfying dessert juice. After all, juice may be exciting and refreshing, but it's hard to measure up to cake and ice cream. This recipe offers some of the same flavors you'll find in a good, natural apple pie, including the spicy zip of cinnamon. That's why it's such a great choice for anyone who craves dessert but prefers a healthy option. Kids love it!

Ingredients:

- 1 medium butternut squash (about 1 ½ pounds)
- 4 medium sweet apples, such as Honey crisp
- 1 teaspoon ground cinnamon

Procedure:

1. Wash the apples and squash to remove dirt and chemical residues. Slice the squash in half, remove the seeds, and cut

the flesh into large cubes. De-seed the apple and remove its stem.

2. Run the apple and the squash cubes through your blender or juicer, adding water as necessary. Stir in the cinnamon and garnish with a cinnamon stick if desired.

3. Drink this enjoyable dessert beverage chilled or warmed.

Slim Summer Cooler
Serves: 2

This fresh juice is full of slender cucumbers and celery, both of which act as natural diuretics to help your body flush out more water. It also contains bright, flavorful apples, ginger and lime. The result is light, refreshing and delightful.

Ingredients:

- 1 large sweet pink apple, such as Pink Lady
- 1 small cucumber
- 1 stalk celery
- ½ Persian lime or 1 Key Lime
- A few ice cubes
- 1 teaspoon fresh ginger

Procedure:

1. Rinse all the ingredients. Remove the stems from the cucumber and apple, along with the apple seeds.

2. Process all ingredients in a juicer to produce an amazing juice with a bright flavor. Serve.

Detox
Serves: 2

The self-cleanse solution!

Ingredients:

- 1 cup water
- 1 tablespoon ginger, peeled, and minced
- 1 apple, cored, and diced
- 1 beet, peeled, and chopped
- 2 carrots, peeled, and chopped

Procedure:

1. Place all the ingredients through the juicer.
2. Add some water and stir to combine.
3. Serve with ice, if preferred.

The All-Rounder
Serves: 2

Improve your overall health!

Ingredients:

- 1 cup spinach
- 1 rib celery, sliced
- 1 apple, cored, and diced
- 4 carrots, peeled, and sliced
- A few strawberries to taste

Procedure:

1. Press the ingredients through a juicer.
2. Stir to combine.
3. Serve with ice, if preferred.

Green Machine Juice Blend
Serves: 2-4

This juice is packed with all the vitamins and minerals you need for sustenance. Not only is it incredibly nutritious, it also has a unique flavor provided by radishes and their greens.

Ingredients:

- 10 red radishes with greens
- 2 plum tomatoes
- 2 medium beets
- 2 small carrots
- 2 large stalks celery
- 2 cups packed parsley leaves

Procedure:

1. Peel, cut, deseed, and/or chop the ingredients as needed.
2. Place a container under the juicer's spout.

3. Feed the ingredients one at a time, in the order listed, through the juicer. Stir the juice and pour into glasses to serve.

Pepper Power
Serves: 2

Spice things up!

Ingredients:

- 1 cup parsley
- 4 red sweet peppers
- 1 slice papaya
- 10 radishes

Procedure:

1. Press the ingredients through a juicer.
2. Stir to combine.
3. Serve with ice, if preferred.

Cucumber Celery Juice
Serves: 2

This recipe is perfect for a juice cleanse or detox because it is low in calories but high in water content. In addition, both cucumber and celery are good sources of healthy nutrients, which will boost the flushing of toxins from your body.

Ingredients:

- 1 large stalks celery
- 1 small head broccoli
- 1 cucumber
- 1/2 small pear
- ½ bunch parsley leaves

Procedure:

1. Peel, cut, deseed, and/or chop the ingredients as needed.
2. Place a container under the juicer's spout.
3. Feed the ingredients one at a time, in the order listed through the juicer.

4. Stir the juice and pour into glasses to serve.

Beet it!
Serves: 2

Take a quick cleanse!

Ingredients:

- 1 cup spinach
- 1 cup blueberries
- 1 cup cranberries
- 2 beetroots
- 1/2 cup coconut water

Procedure:

1. Press the ingredients through a juicer.
2. Add some coconut water and stir to combine.
3. Serve with ice, if preferred.

Ginger Beet Juice
Serves: 2

To make this refreshing juice, you don't even need a juicer. All you have to do is combine the ingredients in your blender and add enough water to reach the desired consistency.

Ingredients:

- 2 medium beets
- 2 large carrots
- 1 medium apple
- 1 cup cold water
- 1-inch piece gingerroot

Procedure:

1. In a blender, combine all of the ingredients and blend until as smooth as possible.
2. Press the mixture through a fine mesh strainer until all of the juice is out.
3. Discard the pulp, pour into glasses, and serve.

Fat Burner
Serves: 2

Reduces cholesterol, cleanses your liver, and stimulates your metabolism!

Ingredients:

- 1 red sweet pepper
- 1 cup celery, sliced
- 5 tomatoes, sliced
- ½ cup radishes
- 1 orange

Procedure:

1. Press the ingredients through a juicer.
2. Stir to combine.
3. Serve with ice, if preferred.

Rockin' Radish Juice
Serves: 2

Radishes are rich in vitamin C, folic acid, and anthocyanin, which make them valuable as a cancer-fighting food. The vegetables in this recipe also contain a combination of vitamins that help to treat skin disorders.

Ingredients:

- 10 small radishes with greens
- 2 cups baby spinach leaves
- 1 large carrot
- 1 large stalk celery
- 1 medium apple
- ½-inch piece gingerroot

Procedure:

1. Peel, cut, deseed, and/or chop the ingredients as needed.

2. Feed the ingredients one at a time, in the order listed through the juicer. Stir the juice and pour into glasses to serve.

Cellulite Shot
Serves: 2

Eliminates toxins and fats!

Ingredients:

- 1 sprig mint
- 1 cup kale
- 1 apple, cored, and sliced
- 1 red bell pepper
- 1 grapefruit, peeled, and chopped

Procedure:

1. Press the ingredients through the juicer.
2. Stir to combine.
3. Serve with ice, if preferred.

Calming Carrot Juice
Serves: 2

This carrot juice is just what you need to help you relax after a long, stressful day. The vitamins and minerals in the ingredients will help your body to recharge and refuel.

Ingredients:

- 5 medium carrots
- 2 large stalks celery
- 1 small orange or grapefruit (the second is better for weight loss as it is low in sugar)

Procedure:

1. Peel, cut, deseed, and/or chop the ingredients as needed.
2. Feed the ingredients one at a time, in the order listed, through the juicer.
3. Stir the juice, dilute in some water or coconut water and pour into glasses to serve.

Power of Pomegranate
Serves: 2

Super refreshing antioxidant drink!

Ingredients:

- 1 pomegranate, seeds only
- 1 apple, cored, and diced
- 2 pears, cored, and diced
- 5 carrots, sliced

Procedure:

1. Press the ingredients through a juicer.
2. Stir to combine.
3. Serve with ice, if preferred.

Carrots and Greens
Serves: 2-4

Great for your bones!

Ingredients:

- ½ apple, cored, and diced
- 2 sprigs parsley
- 1/2 cup kale leaves
- 6 carrots, sliced

Procedure:

1. Press the ingredients through a juicer.
2. Stir to combine.
3. Serve with ice, if preferred.

Pick-Me-Up Juice Blend
Serves: 2

This juice blend is the perfect combination of leafy greens and bright fresh fruit. You get all of the nutritional benefits of kale, dandelion greens, and parsley, and the zesty flavor of green apple and lime.

Ingredients:

- 1 medium green apple
- 8 large kale leaves
- ½ bunch dandelion greens
- ½ bunch parsley leaves
- ½ lime

Procedure:

1. Peel, cut, deseed, and/or chop the ingredients as needed.
2. Feed the ingredients one at a time, in the order listed, through the juicer.
3. Stir the juice and pour into glasses to serve.

Spinach Lime Juice
Serves: 2

If you are in the mood for something fresh and simple, this juice may be just what you need. No muss, no fuss—just delicious.

Ingredients:

- 2 bunches spinach leaves
- 1 medium green apple
- 1 lime

Procedure:

1. Peel, cut, deseed, and/or chop the ingredients as needed.
2. Feed the ingredients one at a time, in the order listed through the juicer.
3. Stir the juice and pour into glasses to serve.

Maximum Greens
Serves: 2

Potassium booster!

Ingredients:

- ½ lemon, peeled
- 1 cup spinach
- 1 cup parsley
- 2 ribs celery, sliced
- 1 apple, cored, and diced
- 3 carrots, sliced

Procedure:

1. Press the ingredients through a juicer.
2. Stir to combine.
3. Serve with ice, if preferred.

Fabulous Fennel Juice Blend
Serves: 2

Fennel is not a vegetable most people have on their shopping list. Though somewhat uncommon, fennel is an excellent source of nutrition. Loaded with calcium, potassium, phosphorus, and vitamin C, it is particularly beneficial for the digestive system.

Ingredients:

- 2 medium fennel bulbs
- 1 small stalk celery
- 1 small carrot
- 1 medium apple

Procedure:

1. Peel, cut, deseed, and/or chop the ingredients as needed.
2. Feed the ingredients one at a time, in the order listed through the juicer.
3. Stir the juice and pour into glasses to serve.

Spicy Tomato Juice
Serves: 2

This spicy tomato juice may be just what you need to bring you out of a funk. Packed with nutrients and the kick of red chili, this is like nothing you've ever tried before.

Ingredients:

- 6 plum tomatoes
- 1 medium red bell pepper
- 1 large carrot
- 1 small cucumber
- 1 red chili pepper

Procedure:

1. Peel, cut, deseed, and/or chop the ingredients as needed.
2. Feed the ingredients one at a time, in the order listed through the juicer.
3. Stir the juice and pour into glasses to serve.

Wrinkle Free
Serves: 1-2

Keep your skin healthy and smooth!

Ingredients:

- 1-inch ginger root
- 2 cucumbers
- 2 grapefruits and 1 lime peeled, and chopped

Procedure:

1. Press the ingredients through a juicer.
2. Stir to combine.
3. Serve with ice, if preferred.

Kick-Start Veggie Juice
Serves: 2

This juice recipe is full of nutritious vegetables to help you kick-start your day. In addition to the health benefits of these vegetables, you also get the crisp, peppery flavor of celery and the freshness of cilantro.

Ingredients:

- 2 large stalks celery
- 1 large carrot
- ½ romaine lettuce heart
- ½ medium cucumber
- 2 sprigs cilantro (very anti-inflammatory)

Procedure:

1. Peel, cut, deseed, and/or chop the ingredients as needed.
2. Feed the ingredients one at a time, in the order listed, through the juicer.
3. Stir the juice and pour into glasses to serve.

Protein Power Juice
Serves: 2

Add a little protein to your favorite juice blends by stirring in a tablespoon of hempseed. Hempseeds are rich in dietary fiber and essential fatty acids.

In fact, hempseeds are a more complete protein source than milk, meat, and eggs.

Ingredients:

- 1 bunch kale leaves
- 1 small head broccoli
- 1 large stalk celery
- ½ bunch collard greens
- 1 tablespoon hempseed

Procedure:

1. Peel, cut, deseed, and/or chop the ingredients as needed.
2. Place a container under the juicer's spout.

3. Feed the first four ingredients one at a time, in the order listed, through the juicer.

4. Stir the hempseed into the juice and pour into glasses to serve.

Skinny Green Juice
Serves: 2

This skinny juice packs a powerful punch. Made with nutritious, low-calorie ingredients like celery and cucumber, this juice will provide your body with a variety of nutrients you need to lose weight almost effortlessly.

Ingredients:

- 2 large stalks celery
- 1 cup romaine lettuce
- 1 cup baby spinach leaves
- 1 cup kale leaves
- 1 small cucumber
- 2 sprigs parsley, dill, or cilantro
- 4 tablespoons freshly squeezed lime juice

Procedure:

1. Peel, cut, deseed, and/or chop the ingredients as needed.
2. Place a container under the juicer's spout.

3. Feed the celery, romaine, spinach, kale, cucumber, and parsley, dill, or cilantro through the juicer.

Stir the lime juice into the juice and pour into glasses to serve.

Carrot Celery Cleanse
Serves: 2

Though carrots and celery are the stars of this recipe, the garlic is not to be forgotten. Garlic helps to regulate blood sugar and cholesterol levels while also providing antimicrobial, antibiotic, and anti-cancer properties.

Ingredients:

- 4 large carrots
- 2 large stalks celery
- 8 large kale leaves
- 1/2 cup spinach leaves
- 1 clove garlic
- 1 green chili

Procedure:

1. Peel, cut, deseed, and/or chop the ingredients as needed.
2. Feed the ingredients one at a time, in the order listed through the juicer.

3. Stir the juice and pour into glasses to serve.

Green Garden Delight
Serves: 2

This recipe is loaded with healthy vegetables, including carrots, celery, bell pepper, and spinach. Spinach is known for its choline content. Choline is a B-complex vitamin that supports cognitive function. These benefits, combined with the nutrients in the other ingredients, create a juice that is perfectly delightful.

Ingredients:

- 2 cups baby spinach leaves
- 1 large carrot
- 1 large stalk celery
- 1 medium green bell pepper
- ½ bunch parsley
- ½ bunch cilantro

Procedure:

1. Peel, cut, deseed, and/or chop the ingredients as needed.

2. Feed the ingredients one at a time, in the order listed through the juicer.

3. Stir the juice and pour into glasses to serve.

Pumpkin Pie Juice
Serves: 2

Rather than reaching for that extra slice of pumpkin pie, try this juice instead! Pumpkin is an excellent source of vitamins C and E, and it also has anti-inflammatory and blood-sugar stabilizing properties.

Ingredients:

- 2 cups pumpkin
- 2 medium apples
- 1 cup cold water
- 1 teaspoon pumpkin pie spice
- 1 teaspoon raw honey

Procedure:

1. Peel, cut, deseed, and/or chop the ingredients as needed.
2. Feed the pumpkin and apples through the juicer.
3. Stir the water, pumpkin pie spice, and honey into the juice and pour into glasses to serve.

Liver Detox Tonic
Serves: 2

Ginger is highly valued for its detoxification properties. In this recipe, it marries perfectly with the nutrients found in kale and bok choy to create a delicious drink that's almost too good to be true.

Ingredients:

- 1 small baby bok choy
- 8 large kale leaves
- 1 medium apple
- 1 small lemon
- ½-inch piece gingerroot

Procedure:

1. Peel, cut, deseed, and/or chop the ingredients as needed.
2. Feed the ingredients one at a time, in the order listed through the juicer.
3. Stir the juice and pour into glasses to serve.

Cucumber Wake-Up Call
Serves: 2

Cucumbers are a good source of B vitamins, which help to regulate blood pressure. Combined with hearty kale, spinach, and the light sweetness of apple, this juice will give you something to wake up for.

Ingredients:

- 2 medium cucumbers
- 2 large kale leaves
- 1 cup baby spinach leaves
- 1 medium apple

Procedure:

1. Peel, cut, deseed, and/or chop the ingredients as needed.
2. Feed the ingredients one at a time, in the order listed through the juicer.
3. Stir the juice and pour into glasses to serve.

Best Foot Forward Juice
Serves: 2

Parsnips are valued for their anti-cancer properties as well as their high levels of iron and calcium. Together with carrots, celery, and cucumber, they help this juice provide you with the nutrition needed to get your day off to a wonderful start.

Ingredients:

- 2 large carrots
- 1 large stalk celery
- 1 medium cucumber
- 1 parsnip with greens
- ½ lemon

Procedure:

1. Peel, cut, deseed, and/or chop the ingredients as needed.
2. Feed the ingredients one at a time, in the order listed through the juicer.
3. Stir the juice and pour into glasses to serve.

Minty Mojito Juice
Serves: 2

The fresh herbs in this juice combine beautifully with zesty lime. If you are craving that mojito flavor, but would rather go for something a little more nutritious, try this!

Ingredients:

- 1 medium cucumber
- ½ cup packed mint leaves
- ½ cup packed basil leaves
- 1 medium apple
- 1 lime

Procedure:

1. Peel, cut, deseed, and/or chop the ingredients as needed.
2. Feed the ingredients one at a time, in the order listed through the juicer.
3. Stir the juice and pour into glasses to serve.

Cool Cilantro Coconut Juice
Serves: 2

This cool juice is just what you need on a hot summer day. Enjoy it while relaxing by the pool, or use it to rehydrate your body after a tough workout.

Ingredients:

- ½ bunch cilantro
- ½ lime
- 4 cups coconut water

Procedure:

1. Peel, cut, deseed, and/or chop the ingredients as needed.
2. Feed the cilantro and lime through the juicer.
3. Stir the coconut water into the juice and pour into glasses to serve.

Summer Squash Supreme
Serves: 2-4

Summer squash is not a vegetable you often see in juicing recipes. It makes a wonderful addition, however, because it is low in calories but high in antioxidants that help repair damage caused by free radicals.

Ingredients:

- 2 cups summer squash
- 1 large apple
- 1 cinnamon sticks
- 2 cups coconut water

Procedure:

1. Peel, cut, deseed, and/or chop the ingredients as needed.
2. Feed the squash and apple through the juicer.
3. Dilute in coconut water.
4. Pour into glasses and serve with the cinnamon sticks.

Beet Berry Blast
Serves: 2

This juice recipe is the perfect combination of nutritious vegetables and fresh fruit flavor. Topped off with a handful of cilantro, this juice is both healthy and refreshing!

Ingredients:

- 3 medium beets
- 2 large stalks celery
- 1½ cups mixed berries
- 1 medium apple
- ½ bunch cilantro leaves

Procedure:

1. Peel, cut, deseed, and/or chop the ingredients as needed.
2. Feed the ingredients one at a time, in the order listed through the juicer.
3. Stir the juice and pour into glasses to serve.

Green Goodness Juice
Serves: 2

This juice is aptly named because it is, after all, full of green goodness. With ingredients like cabbage, cucumber, kale, and green bell pepper, this juice is nothing short of amazing.

Ingredients:

- 1 cup carrots
- 1 cup green, red, or savoy cabbage
- 1 small cucumber
- 1 small green bell pepper
- 1 large kale leaf
- 1 small bunch cilantro

Procedure:

1. Peel, cut, deseed, and/or chop the ingredients as needed.
2. Feed the ingredients one at a time, in the order listed through the juicer.
3. Stir the juice and pour into glasses to serve.

Breakfast of Champions Juice
Serves: 2-4

Carrots are not only the most readily available vegetable, they are also incredibly rich in vitamins and minerals. In addition, carrots also contain beta-carotene and carotenoids, which help reduce the risk for cancer and cardiovascular disease.

Ingredients:

- 4 medium carrots
- 2 small beets
- 2 medium apples
- 2 cups packed baby spinach leaves
- ¼ cup mint leaves

Procedure:

1. Peel, cut, deseed, and/or chop the ingredients as needed.
2. Feed the ingredients one at a time, in the order listed through the juicer.
3. Stir the juice and pour into glasses to serve.

Sweet Potato Power Juice
Serves: 2

Sweet potatoes are known for their unique flavor and their benefits related to detoxification and digestive health. Sweet potatoes are also a good source of copper, iron, manganese, and magnesium.

Ingredients:

- 2 medium apples
- 2 small beets
- 1 large sweet potato
- 1 large carrot
- 1 small red bell pepper

Procedure:

1. Peel, cut, deseed, and/or chop the ingredients as needed.
2. Feed the ingredients one at a time, in the order listed through the juicer.
3. Stir the juice and pour into glasses to serve.

Ginger Green Juice Blend
Serves: 2

Flavored with ginger and sweetened with apple, this juice is something entirely unique and completely refreshing.

Ingredients:

- 1 cup baby spinach leaves
- 1 large carrot
- 1 large stalk celery
- 8 kale leaves
- ½ small cucumber
- 1 medium apple
- 1-inch piece gingerroot

Procedure:

1. Peel, cut, deseed, and/or chop the ingredients as needed.
2. Feed the ingredients one at a time, in the order listed through the juicer.

3. Stir the juice and pour into glasses to serve.

Spirulina Avocado Juice
Serves: 2

Though not your typical juice, this spirulina, avocado blend is packed with essential nutrients. Avocados are an excellent source of heart-healthy fats as well as potassium, which helps regulate blood pressure. Spirulina, cultivated from algae, helps to boost thyroid function.

Ingredients:

- 2 small apples
- 1 seedless cucumber
- 1 ripe avocado
- 1 teaspoon spirulina powder

Procedure:

1. Peel, cut, deseed, and/or chop the ingredients as needed.
2. Place a container under the juicer's spout.
3. Feed the apples and cucumber through the juicer.

4. In a blender or food processor, blend the avocado until smooth.

5. Stir the pureed avocado and spirulina into the juice and pour into glasses to serve.

Before you go, I'd like to remind you that there is a free, complimentary eBook waiting for you. Download it today to treat yourself to healthy, <u>gluten-free desserts and snacks</u> so that you never feel deprived again!

Download link

<u>http://bit.ly/gluten-free-desserts-book</u>

Conclusion

Thank you for reading my book, and thank you for committing to your health. My hope is that you have gained an understanding of how juicing can allow us to feel our best on a daily basis, lose weight naturally, and live disease-free.

The results you will see and feel including sustained energy, decreased mood swings and food sensitivities, increased fitness and so many others, will be the true motivation you need to commit and stay committed.

So... **congratulations!** You have taken an important step. Your body will surely thank you.

If you decide that daily juicing is the lifestyle for you, I hope you will try some of the recipes in this book as you keep experiencing its amazing mind and body benefits. Please let me know your favorites - the review section of this book is an excellent place to share your experience with other readers.

To post an honest review

One more thing... If you have received any value from this book, can you please rank it and post a short review? It only takes a few seconds really and it would really make my day. It's you I am writing for and your opinion is always much appreciated. In order to do so;

1. Log into your account
2. Search for my book on Amazon or check your orders/ or go to my author page at:

http://amazon.com/author/kira-novac

3. Click on a book you have read, then click on "reviews" and "create your review".

Please let me know your favorite motivational tip you learned from this book.

I would love to hear from you!

If you happen to have any questions or doubts about this book, please e-mail me at:

kira.novac@kiraglutenfreerecipes.com

I am here to help.

Recommended Reading

Book Link:

http://bit.ly/spiralizer-book

Recommended Reading

Book Link:

http://bit.ly/weight-loss-motivation-book

FOR MORE HEALTH BOOKS (KINDLE & PAPERBACK) BY KIRA NOVAC PLEASE VISIT:

www.kiraglutenfreerecipes.com/books

Thank you for taking an interest in my work,

Kira and Holistic Wellness Books

HOLISTIC WELLNESS & HEALTH BOOKS

If you are interested in health, wellness, spirituality and personal development, visit our page and be the first one to know about free and 0.99 eBooks:

www.HolisticWellnessBooks.com

Printed in the USA
CPSIA information can be obtained
at www.ICGtesting.com
LVHW050801011123
762209LV00007B/151